GREEN DAY

21ST CENT BREAKDO

CD Art Courtesy of Warner Bros. Records/WEA Corp.
CD Art Design, Photography & Stencils: Chris Bilheimer
Back Cover Photo: Marina Chavez
Cover Inspired by Sixten

© 2009 by Faber Music Ltd
First published in 2009 by Faber Music Ltd
Bloomsbury House 74–77 Great Russell Street London WC1B 3DA
Printed in England by Caligraving Ltd

ISBN10: 0-571-53372-8
EAN13: 978-0-571-53372-5

SING US A SONG OF THE CENTURY

THAT'S LOUDER THAN BOMBS
AND ETERNITY
THE ERA OF STATIC AND CONTRABAND
THAT'S LEADING US TO THE PROMISED LAND
TELL US A STORY THAT'S BY CANDLELIGHT
WAGING A WAR AND LOSING THE FIGHT

THEY'RE PLAYING THE SONG OF THE CENTURY
OF PANIC AND PROMISE AND PROSPERITY
TELL ME A STORY INTO THAT GOODNIGHT

SING US A SONG FOR ME

ACT I

HEROES AND CONS

GREENDAY
21st CENTURY BREAKDOWN

21ST CENTURY BREAKDOWN

BORN INTO NIXON I WAS RAISED IN HELL
A WELFARE CHILD
WHERE THE TEAMSTERS DWELLED
THE LAST ONE BORN,
THE FIRST ONE TO RUN
MY TOWN WAS BLIND FROM REFINERY SUN

MY GENERATION IS ZERO
I NEVER MADE IT
AS A WORKING CLASS HERO

21ST CENTURY BREAKDOWN
I ONCE WAS LOST BUT NEVER WAS FOUND
I THINK I AM LOSING
WHAT'S LEFT OF MY MIND
TO THE 20TH CENTURY DEADLINE

I WAS MADE OF POISON AND BLOOD

CONDEMNATION IS WHAT I UNDERSTOOD

VIDEOGAMES OF THE TOWER'S FALL
HOMELAND SECURITY
COULD KILL US ALL

WE ARE THE CLASS OF '13
BORN IN THE ERA OF HUMILITY
WE ARE THE DESPERATE IN THE DECLINE
RAISED BY THE BASTARDS OF 1969

MY NAME IS NO ONE
THE LONG LOST SON
BORN ON THE 4TH OF JULY
RAISED IN AN ERA OF HEROS AND CONS

THAT LEFT ME FOR DEAD OR ALIVE

I AM A NATION
A WORKER OF PRIDE
MY DEBT TO THE STATUS QUO

THE SCARS ON MY HANDS
AND THE MEANS TO AN END
IS ALL THAT I HAVE TO SHOW

I SWALLOWED MY PRIDE
AND I CHOKED ON MY FAITH
I'VE GIVEN MY HEART AND MY SOUL
I'VE BROKEN MY FINGERS
AND LIED THROUGH MY TEETH
THE PILLAR OF DAMAGE CONTROL

I'VE BEEN TO THE EDGE
AND I'VE THROWN THE BOUQUET
OF FLOWERS LEFT OVER THE GRAVE
I SAT IN THE WAITING ROOM
WASTING MY TIME
AND WAITING FOR JUDGEMENT DAY

I PRAISE LIBERTY
THE "FREEDOM TO OBEY"
IS THE SONG THAT STRANGLES ME
DON'T CROSS THE LINE

DREAM, AMERICA DREAM,
I CAN'T EVEN SLEEP
FROM THE LIGHT'S EARLY DAWN

SCREAM, AMERICA SCREAM
BELIEVE WHAT YOU SEE
FROM HEROS AND CONS?

KNOW YOUR ENEMY

DO YOU KNOW THE ENEMY
DO YOU KNOW YOUR ENEMY
WELL, GOTTA KNOW THE ENEMY

VIOLENCE IS AN ENERGY
AGAINST THE ENEMY
VIOLENCE IS AN ENERGY

BRINGING ON THE FURY THE CHOIR INFANTRY
REVOLT AGAINST THE HONOR TO OBEY

OVERTHROW THE EFFIGY
THE VAST MAJORITY
BURNING DOWN THE FOREMAN OF CONTROL

SILENCE IS THE ENEMY
AGAINST YOUR URGENCY
SO RALLY UP THE DEMONS OF YOUR SOUL

THE INSURGENCY WILL RISE
WHEN THE BLOODS BEEN SACRIFICED
DON'T BE BLINDED BY THE LIES
IN YOUR EYES.

VIOLENCE IS AN ENERGY
FROM HERE TO ETERNITY
VIOLENCE IS AN ENERGY
SILENCE IS THE ENEMY
SO GIMME GIMME REVOLUTION

¡VIVA LA GLORIA!

HEY GLORIA
ARE YOU STANDING CLOSE TO THE EDGE?
LOOK OUT TO THE SETTING SUN
THE BRINK OF YOUR VISION
ETERNAL YOUTH IS
A LANDSCAPE OF THE LIE

THE CRACKS OF MY SKIN CAN PROVE
AS THE YEARS WILL TESTIFY
SAY YOUR PRAYERS AND LIGHT A FIRE
WE'RE GOING TO START A WAR
YOUR SLOGAN'S A GUN FOR HIRE
IT'S WHAT WE WAITED FOR

HEY GLORIA

THIS IS WHY WE'RE ON THE EDGE
THE FIGHT OF OUR LIVES BEEN DRAWN TO
THIS UNDYING LOVE

GLORIA, VIVA LA GLORIA
YOU BLAST YOUR NAME
IN GRAFFITI ON THE WALLS
FALLING THROUGH BROKEN GLASS THAT'S
SLASHING THROUGH YOUR SPIRIT
I CAN HEAR IT LIKE A JILTED CROWD

GLORIA, WHERE ARE YOU GLORIA?
YOU FOUND A HOME
IN ALL YOUR SCARS AND AMMUNITION
YOU MADE YOUR BED IN SALAD DAYS
AMONGST THE RUIN
ASHES TO ASHES OF OUR YOUTH

SHE SMASHED HER KNUCKLES INTO WINTER
AS AUTUMN'S WIND FADES INTO BLACK

SHE IS THE SAINT ON ALL THE SINNERS
THE ONE THAT'S FALLEN THROUGH THE CRACKS
SO DON'T PUT AWAY YOUR BURNING LIGHT

GLORIA, WHERE ARE YOU GLORIA?
DON'T LOSE YOUR FAITH
TO YOUR LOST NAIVETE
WEATHER THE STORM AND DON'T LOOK
BACK ON LAST NOVEMBER
WHEN YOUR BANNERS WERE BURNING DOWN

GLORIA, VIVA LA GLORIA
SEND ME YOUR AMNESTY DOWN
TO THE BROKEN HEARTED
BRING US THE SEASON
THAT WE ALWAYS WILL REMEMBER
DON'T LET THE BONFIRES GO OUT

SO GLORIA,
SEND OUT YOUR MESSAGE OF THE LIGHT
THAT SHADOWS IN THE NIGHT
GLORIA WHERE'S YOUR UNDYING LOVE?
TELL ME THE STORY OF YOUR LIFE

CHRISTIAN'S INFERNO

I GOT UNDER THE GRIP
BETWEEN THE MODERN HELL
I GOT THE REJECTION LETTER IN THE MAIL
AND IT WAS ALREADY RIPPED TO SHREDS.

SEASONS IN A RUIN AND
THIS BITTER PILL IS CHASED WITH BLOOD
THERE'S FIRE IN MY VEINS
AND IT'S POURING OUT LIKE A FLOOD

CHRISTIAN'S INFERNO
CHRISTIAN'S INFERNO

THIS DIABOLIC STATE
IS GRACING MY EXISTENCE

LIKE A CATASTROPHIC BABY
MAYBE MAYBE YOU'RE THE CHEMICAL REACTION
I AM THE ATOM BOMB
I AM THE CHOSEN ONE
TOXIN YOUR RESERVOIR
AND THEN RETURN MAN TO APE

CHRISTIAN'S INFERNO
CHRISTIAN'S INFERNO

BEFORE THE LOBOTOMY

DREAMING
I AM ONLY DREAMING
OF ANOTHER PLACE AND TIME
WHERE MY FAMILY'S FROM

SINGING
I CAN HEAR THEM SINGING
WHEN THE RAIN HAD WASHED AWAY
ALL THESE SCATTERED DREAMS

DYING
EVERYONE'S REMINDED
HEARTS ARE WASHED IN MISERY
DRENCHED IN GASOLINE

LAUGHTER
THERE IS NO MORE LAUGHTER
SONGS OF YESTERDAY
NOW LIVE IN THE UNDERGROUND

LIFE BEFORE THE LOBOTOMY
CHRISTIAN SANG THE EULOGY
SIGN MY LOVE A LOST MEMORY
FROM THE END OF THE CENTURY

WELL IT'S ENOUGH TO MAKE YOU SICK
TO CAST A STONE AND THROW A BRICK
WHEN THE SKY IS FALLING DOWN
IT BURNED YOUR DREAMS INTO THE GROUND

CHRISTIAN'S LESSON

IS WHAT HE'S BEEN SOLD
WE ARE NORMAL AND SELF-CONTROLLED
REMEMBER TO LEARN TO FORGET
WHISKEY SHOTS AND CHEAP CIGARETTES

WELL I'M NOT STONED
I'M JUST FUCKED UP
I GOT SO HIGH I CAN'T STAND UP
I'M NOT CURSED 'CAUSE
I'VE BEEN BLESSED
I'M NOT IN LOVE 'CAUSE I'M A MESS

LIKE REFUGEES
WE'RE LOST LIKE REFUGEES
LIKE REFUGEES
WE'RE LOST LIKE REFUGEES
THE BRUTALITY OF REALITY
IS THE FREEDOM THAT KEEPS ME FROM

DREAMING
I WAS ONLY DREAMING
OF ANOTHER PLACE AND TIME
WHERE MY FAMILY'S FROM.

SINGING
I CAN HEAR THEM SINGING
WHEN THE RAIN HAD WASHED AWAY
ALL THESE SCATTERED DREAMS

DYING
EVERYONE'S REMINDED
HEARTS ARE WASHED IN MISERY
DRENCHED IN GASOLINE

LAUGHTER
THERE IS NO MORE LAUGHTER
SONGS OF YESTERDAY
NOW LIVE IN THE UNDERGROUND

LAST NIGHT ON EARTH

I TEXT A POSTCARD, SENT TO YOU
DID IT GO THROUGH?
SENDING ALL MY LOVE TO YOU
YOU ARE THE MOONLIGHT OF MY LIFE EVERY NIGHT
GIVING ALL MY LOVE TO YOU
MY BEATING HEART BELONGS TO YOU
I WALKED FOR MILES 'TIL I FOUND YOU
I'M HERE TO HONOR YOU
IF I LOSE EVERYTHING IN THE FIRE
I'M SENDING ALL MY LOVE TO YOU.

WITH EVERY BREATH THAT I AM WORTH
HERE ON EARTH
I'M SENDING ALL MY LOVE TO YOU
SO IF YOU DARE TO SECOND GUESS
YOU CAN REST ASSURED
THAT ALL MY LOVE'S FOR YOU

MY BEATING HEART BELONGS TO YOU
I WALKED FOR MILES 'TIL I FOUND YOU
I'M HERE TO HONOR YOU
IF I LOSE EVERYTHING IN THE FIRE
I'M SENDING ALL MY LOVE TO YOU.

MY BEATING HEART BELONGS TO YOU
I WALKED FOR MILES 'TIL I FOUND YOU
I'M HERE TO HONOR YOU
IF I LOSE EVERYTHING IN THE FIRE
DID I EVER MAKE IT THROUGH?

ACT II

CHARLATANS AND SAINTS

GREEN DAY
21st CENTURY BREAKDOWN

RAISE YOUR HANDS NOW TO TESTIFY
YOUR CONFESSION WILL BE CRUCIFIED
YOU'RE A SACRIFICIAL SUICIDE
LIKE A DOG THAT'S BEEN SODOMIZED
STAND UP! - ALL THE WHITE BOYS
SIT DOWN! - AND THE BLACK GIRLS
YOU'RE THE SOLDIERS OF THE NEW WORLD

PUT YOUR FAITH IN A MIRACLE
AND IT'S NON-DENOMINATIONAL
JOIN THE CHOIR WE WILL BE SINGING
IN THE CHURCH OF WISHFUL THINKING

A FIRE BURNS TODAY
OF BLASPHEMY AND GENOCIDE
THE SIRENS OF DECAY
WILL INFILTRATE THE FAITH FANATICS

OH BLESS ME LORD FOR I HAVE SINNED
IT'S BEEN A LIFETIME SINCE I LAST CONFESSED
I THREW MY CRUTCHES IN "THE RIVER
OF A SHADOW OF DOUBT"
AND I'LL BE DRESSED IN MY SUNDAY BEST

SAY A PRAYER FOR THE FAMILY
DROP A COIN FOR HUMANITY
AIN'T THIS UNIFORM SO FLATTERING?
I NEVER ASKED YOU A GOD DAMNED THING

DON'T TEST ME
SECOND GUESS ME
PROTEST ME
YOU WILL DISAPPEAR

EAST JESUS NOWHERE

I WANT TO KNOW WHO'S ALLOWED TO BREED
ALL THE DOGS WHO NEVER LEARNED TO READ
MISSIONARY POLITICIANS
AND THE COPS OF A NEW RELIGION

A FIRE BURNS TODAY
OF BLASPHEMY AND GENOCIDE
THE SIRENS OF DECAY
WILL INFILTRATE THE INSIDE

WELL, I'VE GOT A FEVER
A NON-BELIEVER
I'M IN A STATE OF GRACE
FOR I AM THE CEASAR
I'M GONNA SEIZE THE DAY
WELL, CALL OF THE BANSHEE HEY HEY
HEY HEY HEY HEY HEY
AS GOD AS MY WITNESS
THE INFIDELS ARE GONNA PAY

WELL, CALL THE ASSASSIN
THE ORGASM
A SPASM OF LOVE AND HATE
FOR WHAT WILL DIVIDE US?
THE RIGHTEOUS AND THE MEEK
WELL, CALL OF THE WILD HEY HEY
HEY HEY HEY HEY HEY
DEATH TO THE GIRL
AT THE END OF THE SERENADE

VENDETTA, SWEET VENDETTA
THIS BERETTA OF THE NIGHT
THIS FIRE AND THE DESIRE
SHOTS RINGING OUT ON A HOLY PARASITE

I AM A KILLJOY FROM DETROIT
I DRINK FROM A WELL OF RAGE
I FEED OFF THE WEAKNESS
WITH ALL MY LOVE

CALL UP THE CAPTAIN HEY HEY
HEY HEY HEY HEY HEY
DEATH TO THE LOVER THAT YOU WERE
DREAMING OF

THIS IS A STAND OFF
A MOLOTOV COCKTAIL
ON THE HOUSE
YOU THOUGHT I WAS A WRITE OFF
YOU BETTER THINK AGAIN
CALL THE PEACEMAKER HEY HEY
HEY HEY HEY HEY HEY
I'M GONNA SEND YOU BACK TO THE PLACE
WHERE IT ALL BEGAN

WELL NOW, THE CARETAKER'S
THE UNDERTAKER
NOW I'M GONNA GO OUT
AND GET THE PEACEMAKER
THIS IS THE NEO
ST. VALENTINES MASSACRE
WELL CALL UP THE GAZA HEY HEY
HEY HEY HEY HEY HEY
DEATH TO THE ONES
AT THE END OF THE SERENADE
WELL, DEATH TO THE ONES
AT THE END OF THE SERENADE

PEACEMAKER

LAST OF THE

She puts her makeup on
Like graffiti on the walls of the heartland

She's got her little book of conspiracies
right in her hand
She is paranoid like
endangered species headed into
extinction
She is one of a kind

She's the last of the American girls

She wears her overcoat
For the coming of the nuclear winter
She is riding her bike
Like a fugitive of critical mass
She's on a hunger strike
For the ones who won't make it for dinner

She makes enough to survive
For a holiday of working class

She's a runaway of the establishment
incorporated.
She won't cooperate
She's the last of the American girls

She plays her vinyl records
Singing songs on the eve of destruction
She's a sucker for
All the criminals breaking the laws
She will come in first
For the end of western civilization

She's an endless war
Like a hero for the lost cause
Like a hurricane
In the heart of the devastation
She's a natural disaster
She's the last of the American girls

She puts her makeup on
Like graffiti
On the walls of the heartland
She's got her little book of conspiracies
right in her hand
She will come in first
For the end of western civilization
She's a natural disaster
She's the last of the American girls

AMERICAN GIRLS

¿VIVA LA GLORIA? (LITTLE GIRL)

Little girl, little girl
Why are you crying?
Inside your restless soul
Your heart is dying.
Little one, little one
Your soul is purging
Of love and razor blades
Your blood is surging

Runaway
From the river to the street
And find yourself
With your face in the gutter
Your a stray for the salvation army
There is no place like home
When you got no place to go

Little girl, little girl
Your life is calling
The charlatans and saints
Of your abandon
Little one little one
The sky is falling
The lifeboat of deception
Is now sailing
In the wake all the way
No rhyme or reason

Your bloodshot eyes
Will show your heart of treason
Little girl little girl
You dirty liar
You're just a junkie
Preaching to the choir

Runaway
From the river to the street
And find yourself
With your face in the gutter
Your a stray for the salvation army
There is no place like home
When you got no place to go

The traces of blood
Always follow you home
Like the mascara tears
From your getaway
Your walking with blisters
And running with shears
So unholy,
Sister of grace

MURDER CITY

Desperate
But not hopeless
I feel so useless
In the murder city

Desperate
But not helpless
The clock strikes midnight
In the murder city

I'm wide awake
After the riot
This demonstration
Of our anguish
This empty laughter
Has no reason
Like a bottle
Of your favorite poison

We are the last call
And we're so pathetic

Christian's crying
In the bathroom
And I just want to
Bum a cigarette
We've come so far,
We've been so wasted
It's written
All over our faces

RESTLESS HEART SYNDROME

I've got a really bad disease
It's got me begging on my hands and knees
Take me to the emergency
Cause something seems to be missing
Somebody take the pain away
It's like an ulcer bleeding in my brain
Send me to the pharmacy
So I can lose my memory

I'm elated
Medicated
Lord knows I tried to find a way to run away.

I think they found another cure
For broken hearts and feeling insecure
You'd be surprised what I endure
What makes you feel so self-assured

I need to find a place to hide
You never know what could be waiting outside
The accidents that you could find
It's like some kind of suicide

So what ails you is what impales you
I feel like I've been crucified to be satisfied

I'm elated
Medicated
I am my own worst enemy
So what ails you is what impales you
You are your own worst enemy
You're a victim of the system

I'm a victim of my symptom
I am my own worst enemy
You're a victim of your symptom
You are your own worst enemy
Know your enemy.

ACT
III

HORSESHOES AND HANDGRENADES

GREENDAY
21st CENTURY BREAKDOWN

HORSESHOES AND HANDGRENADES

I'M NOT FUCKING AROUND
I THINK I'M COMING OUT
ALL THE DECEIVERS AND CHEATERS
I THINK WE'VE GOT A BLEEDER RIGHT NOW
WANT YOU TO SLAP ME AROUND
WANT YOU TO KNOCK ME OUT
WELL, YOU MISSED ME KISSED ME
NOW YOU BETTER KICK ME DOWN

MAYBE YOU'RE THE RUNNER UP
BUT THE FIRST ONE TO LOSE THE RACE
ALMOST ONLY REALLY COUNTS IN
HORSESHOES AND HAND GRENADES

I'M GONNA BURN IT ALL DOWN
I'M GONNA RIP IT OUT
WELL, EVERYTHING THAT YOU EMPLOY
WAS MEANT FOR ME TO DESTROY
TO THE GROUND NOW
SO DON'T YOU FUCK ME AROUND
BECAUSE I'LL SHOOT YOU DOWN
I'M GONNA DRINK, FIGHT AND FUCK
AND PUSHING MY LUCK
ALL THE TIME NOW

DEMOLITION, SELF-DESTRUCTION
WHAT TO ANNIHILATE
THE AGE-OLD CONTRADICTION
DEMOLITION, SELF-DESTRUCTION
WHAT TO ANNIHILATE
THE OLD AGE

I'M NOT FUCKING AROUND
I THINK I'M COMING OUT
I'M A HATER A TRAITOR
IN A PAIR OF CHUCK TAYLORS RIGHT NOW
I'M NOT FUCKING AROUND
G-L-O-R-I-A

THE STATIC AGE

CAN YOU HEAR THE SOUND
OF THE STATIC NOISE
BLASTING OUT IN STEREO
CATER TO THE CLASS AND THE PARANOID

MUSIC TO MY NERVOUS SYSTEM
ADVERTISING LOVE AND RELIGION
MURDER ON THE AIRWAVES
SLOGANS ON THE BRINK OF CORRUPTION

VISION OF BLASPHEMY, WAR AND PEACE
SCREAMING AT YOU

I CAN'T SEE A THING IN THE VIDEO
I CAN'T HEAR A SOUND ON THE RADIO
IN STEREO IN THE STATIC AGE

BILLBOARD ON THE RISE
IN THE DAWN'S LANDSCAPE
WORKING YOUR INSANITY
TRAGIC ALA MADNESS AND CONCRETE
COCA COLA EXECUTION
CONSCIOUS ON A CROSS AND
YOUR HEARTS IN A VICE
SQUEEZING OUT YOUR STATE OF MIND
ARE WHAT YOU OWN THAT YOU CANNOT BUY
WHAT A FUCKING TRAGEDY STRATEGY
SCREAMING AT YOU.

HEY HEY IT'S THE STATIC AGE
THIS IS HOW THE WEST WAS WON
HEY HEY IT'S THE STATIC AGE
MILLENIUM

ALL I WANT TO KNOW
IS A GOD DAMNED THING
NOT WHAT'S IN THE MEDICINE
ALL I WANT TO DO IS
I WANT TO BREATHE
BATTERIES ARE NOT INCLUDED
WHAT'S THE LATEST WAY
THAT A MAN CAN DIE
SCREAMING HALLELUJAH?
SINGING OUT
"THE DAWN'S EARLY LIGHT"

THE SILENCE OF THE ROTTEN,
FORGOTTEN
SCREAMING AT YOU

I CAN'T SEE A THING IN THE VIDEO
I CAN'T HEAR A SOUND ON THE RADIO
IN STEREO IN THE STATIC AGE

THE STATIC AGE

21 GUNS

DO YOU KNOW WHAT'S WORTH FIGHTING FOR
WHEN IT'S NOT WORTH DYING FOR?
DOES IT TAKE YOUR BREATH AWAY
AND YOU FEEL YOURSELF SUFFOCATING
DOES THE PAIN WEIGH OUT THE PRIDE?
AND YOU LOOK FOR A PLACE TO HIDE
DID SOMEONE BREAK YOUR HEART INSIDE
YOU'RE IN RUINS

ONE, 21 GUNS
LAY DOWN YOUR ARMS
GIVE UP THE FIGHT
ONE, 21 GUNS
THROW UP YOUR ARMS INTO THE SKY,
YOU AND I

WHEN YOU'RE AT THE END OF THE ROAD
AND YOU LOST ALL SENSE OF CONTROL
AND YOUR THOUGHTS HAVE TAKEN THEIR TOLL
WHEN YOUR MIND BREAKS THE SPIRIT OF YOUR SOUL
YOUR FAITH WALKS ON BROKEN GLASS
AND THE HANGOVER DOESN'T PASS
NOTHING'S EVER BUILT TO LAST
YOU'RE IN RUINS

DID YOU TRY TO LIVE ON YOUR OWN
WHEN YOU BURNED DOWN THE HOUSE AND HOME
DID YOU STAND TOO CLOSE TO THE FIRE?
LIKE A LIAR LOOKING FOR FORGIVENESS FROM A STONE

WHEN IT'S TIME TO LIVE AND LET DIE
AND YOU CAN'T GET ANOTHER TRY
SOMETHING INSIDE THIS HEART HAS DIED
YOU'RE IN RUINS

AMERICAN EULOGY XIII

SING US A SONG OF THE CENTURY
IT SINGS LIKE AMERICAN EULOGY
THE DAWN OF MY LOVE AND CONSPIRACY
FORGOTTEN HOPE AND THE CLASS OF 13
TELL ME A STORY INTO THAT GOOD NIGHT
SING US A SONG FOR ME

A. MASS HYSTERIA

MASS HYSTERIA
RED ALERT IS THE COLOR OF PANIC
ELEVATED TO THE POINT OF STATIC
BEATING INTO THE HEARTS OF THE FANATICS
AND THE NEIGHBORHOOD'S A LOADED GUN
IDLE THOUGHT LEAD TO
FULL THROTTLE SCREAMING
AND THE WELFARE IS ASPHYXIATING
MASS CONFUSION IS ALL THE NEW RAGE
AND IT'S CREATING A FEEDING GROUND
FOR THE BOTTOM FEEDERS OF HYSTERIA

TRUE SOUNDS OF MANIACAL LAUGHTER
AND THE DEAF MUTE IS
MISLEADING THE CHOIR
THE PUNCHLINE IS A NATURAL DISASTER
AND IT'S SUNG BY THE UNEMPLOYED
FIGHT FIRE WITH A RIOT
THE CLASS WAR IS HANGING ON A WIRE
BECAUSE THE MARTYR
IS A COMPULSIVE LIAR
WHEN HE SAID
"IT'S JUST A BUNCH OF NIGGERS
THROWING GAS INTO THE HYSTERIA"

THERE'S A DISTURBANCE ON THE OCEANSIDE
THEY TAPPED INTO THE RESERVE
THE STATIC RESPONSE IS SO UNCLEAR NOW
MAYDAY THIS IS NOT A TEST!
AS THE NEIGHBORHOOD BURNS

AMERICA IS FALLING
VIGILANTES WARNING YA,
CALLING CHRISTIAN AND GLORIA

B. MODERN WORLD

I'M A FUGITIVE SON
IN THE ERA OF DISSENT
A HOSTAGE OF THE SOUL
ON A STRIKE TO PAY THE RENT
THE LAST OF THE REBELS
WITHOUT A COMMON GROUND
I'M GONNA LIGHT A FIRE
INTO THE UNDERGROUND

I DON'T WANT TO LIVE
IN THE MODERN WORLD

I AM A NATION
WITHOUT BUREAUCRATIC TIES
DENY THE ALLEGATION AS IT'S WRITTEN

I WANT TO TAKE A RIDE
TO THE GREAT DIVIDE
BEYOND THE "UP TO DATE"
AND THE NEO-GENTRIFIED
THE HIGH DEFINITION
FOR THE LOW RESIDENT
WHERE THE VALUE OF YOUR MIND
IS NOT HELD IN CONTEMPT
I CAN HEAR THE SOUND OF
A BEATING HEART
THAT BLEEDS BEYOND A SYSTEM
THAT'S FALLING APART
WITH MONEY TO BURN
ON A MINIMUM WAGE
I DON'T GIVE A SHIT
ABOUT THE MODERN AGE

I DON'T WANT TO LIVE
IN THE MODERN WORLD
MASS HYSTERIA

SEE THE LIGHT

I CROSSED THE RIVER
FELL INTO THE SEA
WHERE THE NON-BELIEVERS
GO BEYOND BELIEF
THEN I SCRATCHED THE SURFACE
IN THE MOUTH OF HELL
RUNNING OUT OF SERVICE
IN THE BLOOD I FELL

I JUST WANT TO SEE THE LIGHT
I DON'T WANT TO LOSE MY SIGHT
I JUST WANT TO SEE THE LIGHT
I NEED TO KNOW
WHAT'S WORTH THE FIGHT

I'VE BEEN WASTED
PILLS AND ALCOHOL
I'VE BEEN CHASING
DOWN THE POOL HALLS
I DRANK THE WATER
FROM A HURRICANE
I SET A FIRE
JUST TO SEE THE FLAME

I CROSSED THE DESERT
REACHING HIGHER GROUND
THEN I POUND THE PAVEMENT
TO TAKE THE LIARS DOWN
BUT IT'S GONE FOREVER
BUT NEVER TOO LATE
WHERE THE EVER AFTER
IS IN THE HANDS OF FATE

CONTENTS

SONG OF THE CENTURY

Lyrics by BILLIE JOE
Music by GREEN DAY

Moderately ♩ = 140

Sing us a song of the cen - tu - ry that's

loud - er than bombs and e - ter - ni - ty The er - a of stat - ic and

con - tra - band that's lead - ing us in - to the prom - ised land.

Tell us a sto - ry that's by can - dle - light, wag - ing a war and

los - ing the fight. They're play - ing the song of the cen - tu - ry, of

pan - ic and prom - ise and pros - per - i - ty Tell me a sto - ry in -

rit.

to that good - night. Sing us a song for me.

21st CENTURY BREAKDOWN

*Tune down 1/2 step:
⑥ = E♭   ③ = G♭
⑤ = A♭   ② = B♭
④ = D♭   ① = E♭

Lyrics by BILLIE JOE
Music by GREEN DAY

*Recording sounds one half step lower than written.

14

Faster ♩ = 152 (♫ = ♪³♪)

Instrumental:

*Flick pickup selector switch back and forth while note rings out.

Verse 3:

Verses 4 & 5:

4. My name is no one, the long lost son,
(5.) swal - lowed my pride and I choked on my faith. I've

Rhy. Fig. 1
Elec. Gtr. 2

born on the Fourth of Ju - ly._____
giv - en my heart and my soul._____ I've

end Rhy. Fig. 1

P.M. -

w/Rhy. Fig. 1 *(Elec. Gtr. 2) 3 times*

Raised in the er - a of he - roes and cons, who left me for dead or a -
bro - ken my fin - gers and lied through my teeth, the pil - lar of dam - age con -

live.____ trol.____ I've been to the edge and I've thrown the bou - quet Of

I am a na - tion, a work - er of pride. My

debt to the sta - tus quo.____
flow - ers left o - ver the grave.____ I sat in the wait - ing room,

The scars on my hands and a

means to an end is all that I have____ to show.____
wast - ing my time and wait - ing for Judg - ment

1.

Hey!

Elec. Gtr. 3

Elec. Gtr. 2

Praise lib - er - ty, the "free - dom to o - bey" is the

song that stran - gles me. Well, don't cross the

line.

20

Outro:

dream, A-mer-i - ca,_ dream. I can't e - ven sleep from light's ear - ly_ dawn. Oh,_

Elec. Gtr. 3

Elec. Gtr. 2

scream, A-mer-i - ca,_ scream. Be-lieve what_ you see from he - roes_ and_ cons.

KNOW YOUR ENEMY

Moderately fast ♩ = 132

Lyrics by BILLIE JOE
Music by GREEN DAY

Verse 1:

Bridge 2:

w/Rhy. Fig. 2 *(Elec. Gtr. 1) 2 times*

vi -'lence is an en - er - gy.   (Oh eh, oh eh.)   Well, from here to e - ter - ni - y.

(Oh eh, oh eh.)   Well,   vi -'lence is an en - er - gy,   (Oh eh, oh eh.)   well,

si - lence is the en - e - my, so,   gim - me,   gim - me   rev - o - lu - tion!

Interlude:

Band tacet

Elec. Gtr. 1

Do   you know the en - e - my?   Do you know your en - e - my?   Well,

¡VIVA LA GLORIA!

Lyrics by BILLIE JOE
Music by GREEN DAY

*Elec. Gtr. 1 is a suggested arrangement to emulate the piano.

32

Slower ♩ = 118

BEFORE THE LOBOTOMY

Lyrics by BILLIE JOE
Music by GREEN DAY

when the rain had washed_ a - way_ all these scat-tered dreams._ ___
Songs of yes - ter-day___ now live_ in the un - der - ground._

Interlude:

Elec. Gtr. 1 *(w/light dist.)*

Elec. Gtr. 2 *(w/light dist.)*

Band enters

Elec. Gtr. 2

(Ooh._____)

Verses 3 & 4:

3. Life be - fore the lo - bot - o - my,
4. Chris - tian's les - son's what___ he's been sold.

Chris - tian sang the eu - lo - gy.___
We are nor - mal and self - con - trolled.___

Sign my love a lost___ mem - o - ry,___
Re - mem - ber to learn___ to for - get,___

CHRISTIAN'S INFERNO

Lyrics by BILLIE JOE
Music by GREEN DAY

*Chords are implied.

Christian's Inferno - 4 - 1

46

Christian's Inferno - 4 - 2

Outro:

LAST NIGHT ON EARTH

Lyrics by BILLIE JOE
Music by GREEN DAY

Slowly ♩ = 63

Intro:

1. I text a post-card__ sent to you.__ Did it go through?__
2. With ev-'ry breath__ that__ I am worth__ here on earth,__

52

Last Night on Earth - 5 - 5

EAST JESUS NOWHERE

Lyrics by BILLIE JOE
Music by GREEN DAY

East Jesus Nowhere - 8 - 1

Moderately ♩ = 116 (♫ = ♩♪)

Chorus:

Say a prayer for the family.
Drop a coin for humanity.
Ain't this uniform flattering?
I never asked you a goddamn thing.
(To Chorus:)

PEACEMAKER

Lyrics by BILLIE JOE
Music by GREEN DAY

shots ring-ing out on the ho-ly par-a-site.

3. Well,

end Rhy. Fig. 1

Freely

Band tacet

Acous. Gtr. &
Elec. Gtr. 1

Elec. Gtr. 4 *(w/dist.)*

mf

rake

a tempo
Instrumental:
w/Rhy. Fig. 1 *(Elec. Gtr. 3)*

Acous. Gtr. & Elec. Gtr. 1 resume rhy. fig. simile
Elec. Gtr. 5 *(w/dist.)*

mf

Elec. Gtr. 4

Coda

Freely

Verse 5:
Well, now the caretakers, the undertakers
Saw I'm gonna go out and get a peacemaker.
This is a neo-Saint Valentines massacre.
Well, call up the Gaza, hey, hey, hey, hey, hey, hey, hey.
Well, death to the ones at the end of the serenade.
(To Coda)

LAST OF THE AMERICAN GIRLS

Lyrics by BILLIE JOE
Music by GREEN DAY

Moderately ♩ = 126

Intro:

*Chords are implied.

Verse 1:

3. She plays her

Guitar Solo:

MURDER CITY

Lyrics by BILLIE JOE
Music by GREEN DAY

The clock strikes mid - night in___ the mur - der cit - y.

Guitar Solo:

Elec. Gtr. 1 resume chorus fig. simile

Riff A

Elec. Gtr. 2 *(w/light dist.)*

mf

1. **Em**

2. **Em**   *D.S. ℅ al Coda*

end Riff A

¿VIVA LA GLORIA?
(LITTLE GIRL)

Lyrics by BILLIE JOE
Music by GREEN DAY

Moderately slow ♩ = 84

Moderately, in 2 ♩ = 96

Piano cont. simile

Verse 1:

Lit - tle girl, lit - tle girl, why are you cry - ing?

In - side your rest - less soul___ your heart is dy - ing.

Lit - tle one, lit - tle one, your soul is purg - ing,

of love and ra - zor blades_ your blood is surg - ing. Run a -

¿Viva la Gloria? (Little Girl) - 8 - 1

82

Chorus:

RESTLESS HEART SYNDROME

*All gtrs. tuned down 1 whole step:
⑥ = D   ③ = F
⑤ = G   ② = A
④ = C   ① = D

Lyrics by BILLIE JOE
Music by GREEN DAY

1. I've got a real-ly bad__ dis- ease.
2. I think they found an-oth-er cure

*Recording sounds one whole step lower than written.

*Strum pattern for Acous. Gtr.
Acous. Gtr. tacet 8 meas. first time only (enter at meas. 13)
Second time, play through entire verse.

Restless Heart Syndrome - 7 - 1

Pre-chorus:

Chorus:

Guitar Solo:

94 *Chorus:*

HORSESHOES AND HANDGRENADES

Lyrics by BILLIE JOE
Music by GREEN DAY

*Chords are implied (meas. 14–17)

Verses 1 & 2:

*Chords are implied (meas. 63–70)

Interlude:

Verse 3:

w/Rhy. Fig. 1 *(Elec. Gtrs. 1 & 2) 2 times, simile*

THE STATIC AGE

Intro:

Lyrics by BILLIE JOE
Music by GREEN DAY

*Composite arrangement.
**Chords are implied.

Verses 1 & 2:

w/Rhy. Fig. 1 *(Elec. Gtr. 1)*

1. Can you hear the sound of the stat - ic noise,___ blast - ing out in
2. Bill - board on the rise in the dawn's land - scape,___ work - ing your in -

ste - re - o? Ca - ter to the class and the par - a -
san - i - ty. Trag - ic à la mad - ness and con -

The Static Age - 7 - 1

in ste-re-o in the__ stat - ic__ age.____

w/Rhy. Fig. 1 *(Elec. Gtr. 1)*

*Chords are implied. Elec. Gtr. 2 tacet.

D.S. %

I can't see a thing in the vid - e - o.

I can't hear a sound on the ra - di - o in ste - re - o

in the__ stat - ic__ age.____

Verse 3:

Elec. Gtr. 1

Elec. Gtr. 3

All I want to know is a god-damned thing,_ not what's in the med - i-cine.

8va throughout

Cont. rhy. simile

All I want to do is I want to breathe,_ bat-ter-ies are not in-clud-ed.

Chorus:

21 GUNS

Lyrics by BILLE JOE
Music by GREEN DAY

Moderately slow ♩ = 84

Intro:

*To simulate volume pedal effect: With volume turned down on guitar, hammer both notes with left hand while gradually turning up the volume knob on the guitar to create bowed effect, then gradually turn volume down. Repeat for each note group.

Verses 1 & 3:

1. Do you know what's worth fight - ing for, _____ when it's not worth
3. When you're at the end of the road, _____ and you lost all

dy - ing for? _____ Does it take your breath _____ a - way _____ and you feel _____
sense of con - trol. _____ And your thoughts have tak - en their toll, _____ when your mind _____

114

Guitar Solo:

Cont. rhy. simile

Band tacet

Interlude:

Band cont. tacet

Verse 5:

When it's time to___ live and let die,___ and you can't get an - oth - er try.___

Some - thing in - side this heart__ has died,___ you're in ru - ins.

Elec. Gtr. 1

Band re-enters

Chorus:

Elec. Gtr. 2 & Acous. Gtr. resume chorus fig. simile

One,   twen - ty - one guns,___   lay down your arms,___   give up the fight.___

(Ah._____

One,   twen - ty - one guns,___   throw up your arms__

___   )

Elec. Gtr. 3

___   in - to the sky._____   One,   twen - ty - one guns,___

(Ah._____   )

AMERICAN EULOGY
(A. Mass Hysteria - B. Modern World)

Lyrics by BILLIE JOE
Music by GREEN DAY

Moderately ♩ = 140

Sing us the song___ of the cen - tu - ry, it

sings like A - mer - i - can eu - lo - gy. The

dawn of my love and con - spir - a - cy of

for - got - ten hope and the class of thir - teen.

Tell me a sto - ry in - to that good - night,

Faster ♩ = 160

sing us a song___ for me.___ Hys -

A. Mass Hysteria

*On the recording Acous. Gtr. is tuned down 1/2 step and played with open chords in the key of D,
but for this arrangement, Acous. Gtr. was arranged to play in concert key to keep all guitars in standard tuning.

B. Modern World

Chorus:

I don't want to live   in the mod - ern world,   I don't want to live   in the mod - ern world.

I don't want to live   in the mod - ern world,   I don't want to live   in the mod - ern world. Well, I'm the

*Chords implied by bass gtr.

SEE THE LIGHT

Lyrics by BILLIE JOE
Music by GREEN DAY

Moderately fast ♩ = 138

Intro:

Verse 1:

w/Rhy. Figs. 1 *(Piano)* **& 1A** *(Elec. Gtr. 1)*, both 8 times, simile

crossed the riv - er,____ fell in - to the sea,____ where the

non - be - liev - ers____ go be - yond be - lief.____ Then I

Band enters

Rhy. Fig. 2
Elec. Gtr. 2 *(w/light dist.)*

end Rhy. Fig. 2

scratched the sur - face_____ in the mouth of hell,___ run - ning

out of ser - vice,_____ in the blood I fell.___ Well, I,___

Elec. Gtr. 1

Fill 1 - - - - - - - - - - - - -
Elec. Gtr. 3 *(w/light dist.)*

trem. pick - - - - - - - - - - - - -

* Tremolo pick in a 16th-note pattern while
sliding left-hand finger down string.

I just want___ to see___ the light._____

And I___

need to know___what's worth___ the fight._____

D.S. % al Coda

3. Well, I

Elec. Gtr. 2

⊕ Coda

__ what's worth__ the fight._____

Elec. Gtr. 2

Elec. Gtr. 1

Outro:

Repeat and fade

Band tacet

TABLATURE EXPLANATION

TAB illustrates the six strings of the guitar.
Notes and chords are indicated by the placement of fret numbers on each string.

String ⑥, 3rd fret   String ①, 12th fret   A "C" chord   C chord arpeggiated
                   String ③, 13th fret

BENDING NOTES

Half Step:
Play the note and bend string one half step (one fret).

Whole Step:
Play the note and bend string one whole step (two frets).

Slight Bend/ Quarter-Tone Bend:
Play the note and bend string sharp.

Prebend and Release:
Play the already-bent string, then immediately drop it down to the fretted note.

Bend and Release:
Play the note and bend to the next pitch, then release to the original note. Only the first note is attacked.

PICK DIRECTION

Downstrokes and Upstrokes:
The downstroke is indicated with this symbol (⊓) and the upstroke is indicated with this (∨).

ARTICULATIONS

Hammer On:
Play the lower note, then "hammer" your finger to the higher note. Only the first note is plucked.

Pull Off:
Play the higher note with your first finger already in position on the lower note. Pull your finger off the first note with a strong downward motion that plucks the string—sounding the lower note.

Palm Mute:
The notes are muted (muffled) by placing the palm of the pick hand lightly on the strings, just in front of the bridge.

Muted Strings:
A percussive sound is produced by striking the strings while laying the fret hand across them.

Legato Slide:
Play the first note and, keeping pressure applied on the string, slide up to the second note. The diagonal line shows that it is a slide and not a hammer-on or a pull-off.

HARMONICS

Natural Harmonic:
A finger of the fret hand lightly touches the string at the note indicated in the TAB and is plucked by the pick producing a bell-like sound called a harmonic.

RHYTHM SLASHES

Strum Marks/ Rhythm Slashes:
Strum with the indicated rhythm pattern. Strum marks can be located above the staff or within the staff.

Single Notes with Rhythm Slashes:
Sometimes single notes are incorporated into a strum pattern. The circled number below is the string and the fret number is above.

Artificial Harmonic:
Fret the note at the first TAB number, lightly touch the string at the fret indicated in parens (usually 12 frets higher than the fretted note), then pluck the string with an available finger or your pick.